Going to
Grandma's

PaRragon
Bath · New York · Singapore · Hong Kong · Cologne · Delhi
Melbourne · Amsterdam · Johannesburg · Auckland · Shenzhen

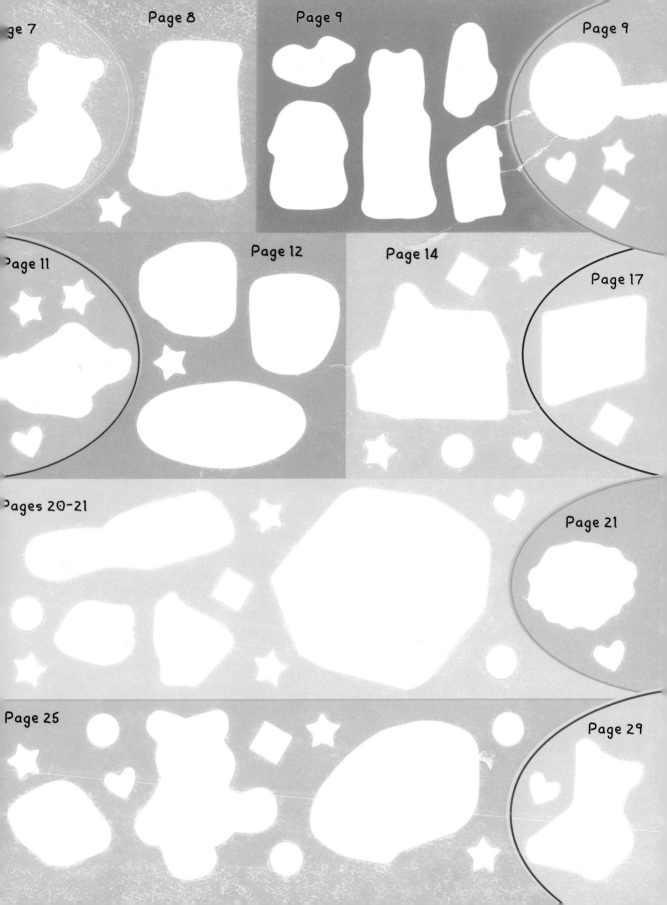

Page 7

Page 8

Page 9

Page 9

Page 11

Page 12

Page 14

Page 17

Pages 20-21

Page 21

Page 25

Page 29

How to Use This Book

 Read the story, all about Sam's first sleepover at his grandma's house.

 Look closely at each picture in the story. You may be asked to find or count things in a scene and place a sticker on the page.

 Try each activity as you go along, or read the story first, then go back and do the activities. The answers are at the bottom of each activity page.

 Some pictures will need stickers to finish the scenes or activities. Any leftover stickers can be used to decorate the book or your things.

Sam is going to stay at Grandma's house for a few days.

Find these things in Sam's bedroom.

He doesn't know what he'll need.
Good thing Mom is here to help him pack!

Now put Sam's teddy bear sticker here.

Mom helps Sam choose the clothes to pack in his suitcase.

Find the sticker of Sam's pants to finish the picture.

Look at the words below and count the clothes in the main picture. Then add the stickers to match.

single sock

underpants

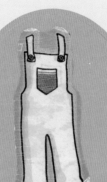

overalls

T-shirts

shorts

Answers

6 single socks, 1 pair of overalls,
3 pairs of underpants,
2 pairs of shorts, and 2 T-shirts

Now find the sticker of Sam and put it here.

Sam wants to put some of his favorite
books and toys in his backpack.

Can you find these things in Sam's bedroom?

"Is anything missing?" asks Mom. "Yes!" says Sam. "Teddy!" So Teddy is packed too.

That afternoon, Grandma comes to collect Sam.
She has a cup of coffee with Mom in the kitchen.

Find the stickers
to finish the
picture.

Sam goes to get his things.
"Teddy can ride along," says Sam.

Grandma and Sam walk to Grandma's house. Can you help them get there?

Answer

Put the sticker of Grandma's house in the maze to finish the picture.

These two pictures of Grandma's house may look the same, but there are six differences between them.
Can you find them?

Answer

At Grandma's house, Grandma shows Sam where he will sleep. There is a picture of Mommy and Daddy right next to Sam's bed.

Can you find these things in the bedroom?

"Would you like to put Teddy on the bed?" asks Grandma. Sam holds Teddy tightly. "He might be lonely in here all by himself," he says.

Now find the sticker of Sam's baby picture.

Sam is hungry, so Grandma fixes a snack
for him. It is peanut butter and jelly,
with a glass of milk—Sam's favorite.

Grandma cuts the sandwich into four pieces,
just like Mommy does.

Answer

After his snack, Sam helps Grandma with some gardening. Teddy comes, too!

Find the stickers to finish the picture.

Can you find these things in Grandma's garden?

Sam helps Grandma pull the weeds out.
Then they cut some flowers to put on the table.

Put the flower
sticker here.

Later, Sam draws a picture of Grandma while she makes dinner.

Then he draws a special picture of the
two of them, for her to keep.

Draw lines to match each pair.

Answer

24

After dinner, Grandma and Sam play a game in the living room. "I win!" shouts Sam.

Bath time! Grandma helps Sam get nice and clean after his busy day.

Can you find five differences between these two pictures?

Answer

Point to the differences.

At bedtime, Grandma reads Sam
a story from one of the books he has
brought with him.

Can you find these things in the bedroom?

"Night-night, sweet dreams," Grandma says as she tucks Sam and Teddy into their cozy bed.

Now put the teddy bear sticker here.

"I like staying with you, Grandma," Sam says.
"And I think Teddy does, too!"